GETTING
STARTED IN
MINERAL
COLLECTING

BOOKS IN THE Getting Started SERIES

Getting Started in Mineral Collecting

BARBARA H. AMLICK

COLLIER BOOKS | NEW YORK, NEW YORK

COLLIER-MACMILLAN LTD. | LONDON

*The Macmillan Company
866 Third Avenue, New York, N.Y. 10022
Collier-Macmillan Canada Ltd., Toronto, Ontario*

Library of Congress Catalog Card Number: 78-183404

First Collier Books Edition 1972

Printed in the United States of America

Acknowledgments

The author wishes to express her deep appreciation
to T. L. Baskin and Sons of Middlesex,
New Jersey, who so kindly loaned a number of
the minerals that appear in the color photographs.

Contents

Preface

There are close to three million people in the United States who collect minerals as a hobby. They come from every walk of life; some are senior citizens, many are young people and children. The majority of mineral collectors are amateurs with no professional interest or formal training in mineralogy. Many of them started out with little or no previous knowledge of minerals. Some have since become experts in mineralogy, others have gone on to become professionals, and many own specimens as fine as those seen in museum collections; all have learned something from their collecting experience.

There is a wealth of knowledge to be gained from collecting minerals, yet the only prerequisite demanded by this hobby is a lively curiosity. Anyone who has ever picked up an attractive pebble and wondered what it was made of, or where it originated, is a potential mineral collector. There are probably many people who, though interested in minerals, have resisted the temptation to collect them simply because they do not know how to get started. It is primarily for these people that this book is intended.

Getting Started in Mineral Collecting is essentially a guide to the hobby of collecting minerals. It is not a mineralogy textbook nor is it a guide to the minerals themselves or to the localities where they are found. Although the physical and chemical properties of minerals are described in general, the properties of individual species are beyond the scope of a book of this size. Space also limits the discussion of crystallography, or the basic crystal systems.

The main purpose of this book is to assist the novice in finding and identifying specimens and in starting a mineral collection of his own. A great deal of emphasis has been placed on rocks since, for the collector as well as the prospector, rocks hold the clues necessary for locating mineral deposits. The various tests and procedures that are useful for identifying minerals have been included, as has information about tools and other basic equipment. There is also a section devoted to the trimming, cleaning, and cataloging of specimens. Most of the photographs show rather ordinary specimens such as a beginner might find or easily acquire through purchase or trade.

GETTING
STARTED IN
MINERAL
COLLECTING

Starting a Mineral Collection | 1

There are presently nearly two thousand different minerals which have been found and identified, and which are recognized as separate and distinct species. Many of these minerals occur in more than one form, and they may vary in color and crystal shape as well. Every now and then someone discovers a new mineral, so the list of known species and varieties continues to grow.

Some minerals are very common and can be found almost any place in the world. Many are less common and occur only in certain localities that for various reasons were favorable to their development. Other minerals are considered rare, and a small number are known to science by only a few specimens.

Because of the great number of minerals and mineral varieties, it is unlikely that any collector can acquire specimens of all of them. Most mineral collectors set quality rather than quantity as their goal, and concentrate their efforts on knowing fewer species well.

Types of Collections

Mineral collections fall into two categories: general and special. A general collection consists of a variety of minerals, specimens of which may come from a nearby locality or from as far away as Africa, India, or

New South Wales. Rocks, fossils, and other related material are often included, for the scope of a general collection is practically limitless.

Most hobbyists start out with a general collection. The beginner can learn a great deal from a collection of this type, particularly if he has no previous knowledge of minerals. It not only gives him the opportunity to see and handle many different kinds of minerals, but also allows him to compare the physical properties of one species with those of another.

Later, as the collector becomes more familiar with minerals, he often finds that his interest focuses on some particular mineral, mineral group, or collecting site; when this happens, he may choose to specialize. For instance, he may collect only those minerals found in the area in which he lives; or those from a single mine, mining district, county, or state. If representative, regional collections can be of considerable scientific value and are the ones most eagerly sought by museums.

The collector may specialize in one class of minerals, such as the sulfides; or he may narrow his field down to a single species—possibly

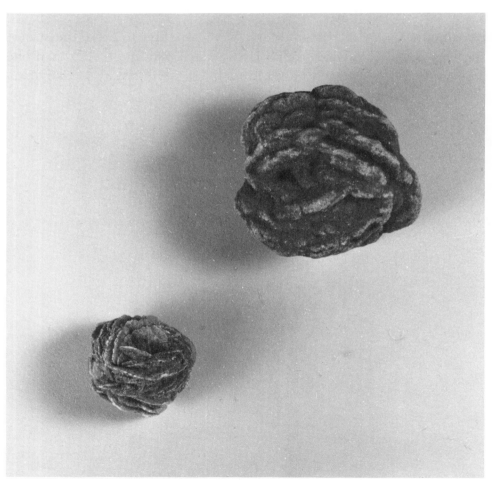

Barite (desert rose) from Las Cruces, New Mexico. *Hoppock Associates*

quartz or calcite. Some hobbyists confine their collecting to gem minerals; others collect only single crystals; still others specialize in pseudomorphs (see page 58) or other unusual forms. Not only are there numerous possibilities for specialization, but one or more special collections are often included within the broader framework of a general collection.

Specimen Size

When planning a mineral collection, some thought should be given to the size of the specimens to be included. Specimen size may seem unimportant to the beginner who has yet to acquire his first minerals; but as his own collection grows, he will soon come to appreciate the fact that even small mineral specimens take up space and also add considerable weight to cabinet drawers, shelves, and floor beams. Since most of us live in small houses or even smaller apartments that afford only a minimum of space for storing and displaying minerals, it is wise to consider the amount of space available for a collection and to limit the size of specimens accordingly. Through lack of such planning, more than one avid mineral collector has found himself faced with the choice of abandoning his hobby or moving to larger quarters. Many collectors specialize in specimens of a certain size; others try to keep specimens within a limited range of sizes. Some uniformity in the size of specimens will make a more attractive collection. It is important to be acquainted with the following terms used to describe specimen sizes:

Handsize (4 by 5 inches) specimens are particularly good for cabinet display, and for this reason they have been popular with collectors. Fine handsize specimens, however, are usually expensive, and in the case of some of the rarer minerals, may be priced beyond the means of the average collector.

Standard (3 by 4 inches) mineral specimens are widely used in the reference collections of schools, colleges, and museums. This specimen size is also popular with many private collectors. It is particularly good for regional material, ore minerals, and rocks.

Miniatures (1½ by 2 inches) and specimens measuring 2 by 3 inches are probably the most suitable for home collections. Both sizes are large enough for display, yet small enough to store easily in cabinet drawers and boxes.

Thumbnails (1 by 1 inch), though small, are excellent for someone who specializes in rare minerals, or who has only a very limited amount of storage space. Thumbnail specimens are widely used by schools and colleges in connection with earth science and geology courses; and because they are moderately priced, they are popular with children.

Micromounts are specimens usually of crystallized minerals that are small enough to fit into a standard plastic or cardboard micromount box. Because very small crystals are often more perfect in form than larger ones, there has been a growing interest among collectors in micromount specimens. Their main disadvantage is that, to be fully appreciated, they must be viewed with a stereomicroscope.

Museum-size is a term used by mineral dealers and collectors for any large specimen; it does not necessarily mean that such a specimen is museum "quality." *Cabinet-size* is another term similarly used. There

Pisolitic hematite from Gila County, Arizona. *Hoppock Associates*

is no doubt that a museum-size specimen of fine quality is impressive when displayed alone or with other specimens of the same size. However, in a collection of smaller specimens, it tends to look out-of-scale.

Buying Specimens

A beginner often asks, "Should I buy minerals?"

Although there are hobbyists who limit their collections to specimens they find themselves, the average collector generally buys some of his minerals. Just how many specimens a collector buys depends, of course, on where he lives, the type of minerals he collects, and the amount of time and money he can devote to his hobby. A collector usually tries to find as many minerals as possible on his own. Occasionally he will buy a hard-to-find specimen from a dealer, and he gets others by trading with fellow collectors. Trading is an excellent way to acquire minerals one might not otherwise find or be able to afford.

The overall quality of a specimen is the most important thing to consider when buying minerals. It should be noted that the quality of a mineral specimen has nothing to do with its size. Thus a large specimen that is poorly shaped or damaged may be less desirable than a small one in fine condition. Until the beginner has gained some experience in selecting minerals, he would be wise to purchase only moderately-priced specimens of the more common minerals.

Basic Equipment

The hobbyist who plans to do some collecting in the field will need certain basic equipment. Collecting equipment is sold by many mineral dealers, or it can be ordered from scientific suppliers such as Ward's Natural Science Establishment in Rochester, New York. Gads, sledges, and other suitable tools may be available at local hardware stores.

The most essential tool for collecting minerals is a *geologist's hammer*—either a standard pick hammer, or one with a chisel-shaped cutting edge. A pick hammer is usually the best for working in pegmatites and other "hard" rock formations. The hammer should be made of well-tempered steel, with a square striking face and cutting edge at right angles to the handle (Figure 1). Some collectors prefer an all-metal hammer; others prefer one with a wooden or fiberglass handle. Each has certain advantages and disadvantages. Generally speaking, a hammer with a wooden or fiberglass handle is lighter, easier to carry, and more comfortable in the hand; while an all-metal hammer is more durable,

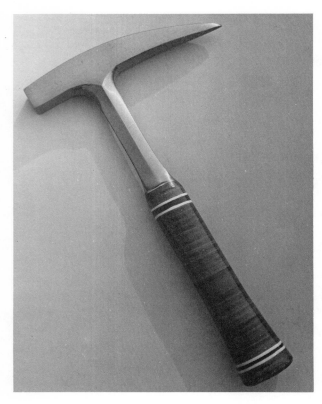

FIGURE 1 A standard geologist's pick hammer. *Hoppock Associates*

particularly in hot, dry climates. Geologist's hammers also come in several weights; the choice is a matter of personal preference.

Safety goggles or a protective eye shield should always be worn when hammering, chipping, or trimming rock. Wearing such goggles is the best way to avoid serious eye injuries that may result from flying slivers of rock or tool steel. Plastic safety goggles such as the ones shown in Figure 2 are inexpensive, lightweight, and designed to fit easily over regular eyeglasses.

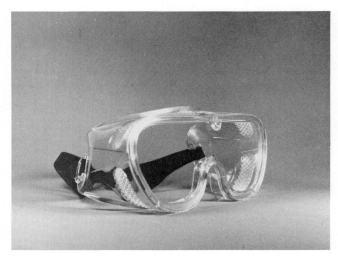

FIGURE 2 Safety goggles made of clear, flexible plastic provide all-around protection for the eyes. *Hoppock Associates*

Some sort of *hand magnifier* is indispensable for examining and identifying specimens. Small magnifiers are available in various styles but the pocket variety, with a lens that folds into a protective metal case (Figure 3), is usually the best for use in the field. Hand magnifiers are available in 5x to 20x magnifications. The higher the magnification of a lens, however, the smaller and narrower its field of view. Thus lenses

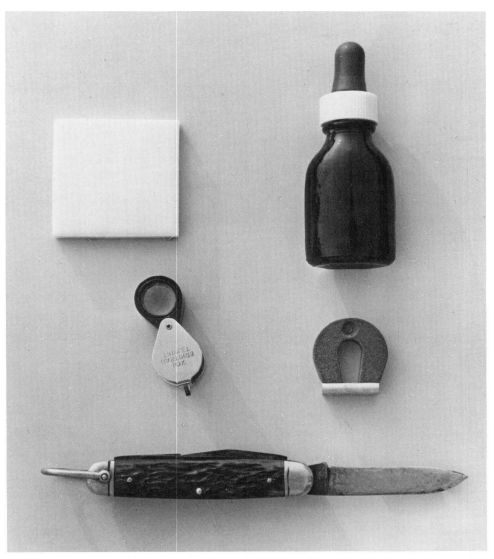

FIGURE 3 Some small items of equipment which mineral collectors find essential include a penknife, hand magnifier, Alnico magnet, and streak plate. A small bottle with a dropper is useful for holding the acid needed for carbonate testing. *Hoppock Associates*

above 10x are not recommended for mineral work. It is important that the lens selected be corrected both for color and for spherical aberration. A good "used" magnifier can sometimes be purchased from a dealer in second-hand optical equipment.

A *collecting bag* for transporting specimens and collecting equipment is another essential. The bag should be made of canvas or heavy cotton duck and have an adjustable shoulder strap. A knapsack of the type used by the Boy Scouts is also suitable.

In addition to the equipment mentioned, a mineral collector needs a good penknife, a small Alnico magnet, an unglazed white tile (Figure 3), and some kind of notebook for recording collecting data.

Other Useful Equipment

Until he has had time to familiarize himself with the various practices and techniques employed in field collecting, it is unnecessary for a beginner to buy more than the basic equipment. Later, if the need arises, he may wish to add some of the following tools to his store of equipment:

A *crack hammer* (Figure 4) is essentially a lightweight, short-handled sledge. It is useful for breaking up tough rock, striking chisels, driving wedges and gads, and for general trimming purposes. In a hammer of this type, a one-piece, all-metal construction is the most practical because it eliminates any danger of the head loosening and flying off. Crack hammers are available in weights of two, three, and four pounds.

A *chipping hammer* is similar to a geologist's hammer but it doesn't have a flat striking face. It combines a vertical blade at one end of the head with a standard pick at the other. A chipping hammer is particularly good for working in sedimentary rock, and for this reason fossil hunters often prefer it to the more conventional geologist's hammer.

Gad-point chisels (Figure 5) of various lengths and diameters are extremely effective for splitting and prying apart rock. For this purpose most collectors prefer gads to steel wedges, which have a tendency to "mushroom" with hard use. Wedge-bladed *cold chisels* (Figure 5) have more limited use in the field, although small ones are sometimes helpful in removing delicate crystal linings from cavities. Cold chisels and gads are used extensively for hand-trimming and shaping specimens. A broad-bladed chisel, called a *pitching tool* (Figure 5), is also helpful for trimming and shaping.

A modified pry bar known to mineral collectors as a *pocket robber* is unexcelled where considerable leverage is needed for prying or moving large rocks. Pocket robbers are made from standard hexagonal bar

FIGURE 4 An all-metal crack hammer with a nonslip nylon-vinyl handgrip. *Hoppock Associates*

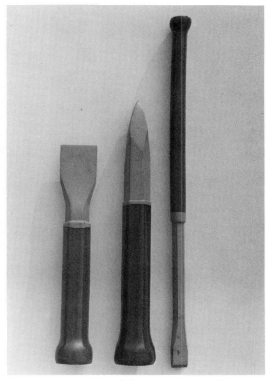

FIGURE 5 (*left to right*) A broad-bladed chisel, or pitching tool; a gad-point chisel; and a small cold chisel. *Hoppock Associates*

stock of various lengths. The ends are tapered and bent over slightly in opposite directions. A bar about two feet in length is good and not too cumbersome to carry.

In some situations, a *shovel* may be needed for digging or removing loose rubble. The blade of the shovel should be fairly shallow in depth, and pointed rather than rounded at the tip. A small folding entrenching shovel similar to the type used by the U.S. Army is ideal.

On occasion the collector may find a *gold pan* useful for recovering heavy minerals and small gemstones from stream gravels. A black, sheet-iron pan about sixteen inches in diameter is recommended. Some models come equipped with a foam-rubber pad designed to trap small particles in the bottom of the pan. Strong arms and a good deal of practice are needed to use a gold pan efficiently.

Brown, reticulated, cerussite specimen from Tsumeb, South West Africa. *Hoppock Associates*

Screens and *sieves* of various mesh sizes can be used for separating small mineral fragments from dry soil, clay, or gravel. The exact size of the screen mesh must, of course, be determined by the size of the particles to be recovered. If the hobbyist is handy with a saw and hammer, simple hand-screens can be homemade from scrap lumber. Suitable screen mesh can be purchased by the yard at most hardware stores.

Small garden tools such as hand-weeders and cultivators can often be used for digging in loose soil or mine-dump rubble. Other tools and common items found in the average home may also prove useful. Improvised equipment is more often the mark of an experienced collector rather than a beginner.

References

Every collector needs a good book on minerals for reference. The most useful is one that describes in some detail the occurrence, physical properties, and chemical composition of the more common minerals. It need not include descriptions of minor subspecies or rare minerals that are seldom encountered in the field. If the book contains photographs, these should be of representative specimens. Determinative tables for mineral identification can be extremely useful. Books for reference as well as others that may be of interest to mineral collectors are listed on pages 91-92.

Rocks | 2

"Begin with rocks" is the best advice that can be offered the novice collector. Success in locating minerals, whether they be specimens for a collection or workable ore deposits, depends largely on knowing where to look for them. All minerals are found in rocks or in situations closely related to rocks; therefore, it stands to reason that if the collector wants to find minerals, he must first learn to recognize the rocks in which they occur.

What Is a Rock?

Rocks are the essential materials—the bricks and mortar, so to speak—that make up the earth's crust. Although most rocks are aggregates of two or more minerals, some are *monomineralic* (composed of one mineral). Quartz, for example, consists of a single mineral; but because it is so widespread as to actually form part of the earth's structure, quartz is considered a rock. Natural glass is also a rock, though its composition is extremely variable.

There are more than six hundred types of rocks; however, only the most common and representative ones will be discussed here. It should be mentioned that one type of rock frequently grades into another type, and a range of intermediate types is not uncommon. For this reason many rocks cannot be positively identified without detailed laboratory study. In the field, rocks are generally identified on the basis of their physical appearance and a few simple tests. Though field identification is somewhat arbitrary, is should serve the needs of the collector.

Based on the manner in which they were formed, rocks are divided into three groups: *igneous, sedimentary,* and *metamorphic.* Since each group has certain distinguishing characteristics, the collector, after some practice, should have little difficulty in recognizing the group to which a rock belongs.

Igneous Rocks

Igneous rocks are formed directly from *magma*—a hot, molten material that originates far below the earth's surface. Magma contains the various chemical elements that crystallize to form minerals as the magma cools. The bulk of all igneous rocks is made up of only seven minerals and mineral groups. Certain other minerals may also be present, but these occur in such small amounts that they are termed *accessory minerals.* Igneous rocks in which quartz, feldspars, and the felds-

Phlogopite mica from Pine Island, Orange County, New York. *Hoppock Associates*

pathoids predominate are light in color; those in which the *ferromagnesian* minerals (olivine, amphiboles, pyroxenes, and biotite mica) predominate are much darker and have a higher specific gravity (see page 64). Light-colored igneous rocks are also known as *acidic rocks*, and the dark-colored ones as *basic rocks*.

Igneous rocks are subdivided into *intrusive* (plutonic) and *extrusive* (volcanic) rocks, depending on whether they solidified above or below ground. Intrusives are those rocks formed from magma that has cooled and hardened at various depths within the earth's crust. In texture, intrusives are much coarser than extrusives, although in chemical composition, the rocks are identical. The texture of an igneous rock is largely governed by the rate at which it cools. In the case of intrusives, the older rock surrounding the molten magma acts as insulation, slowing down the cooling process and thus allowing more time for the individual mineral grains to increase in size. As a rule, the greater the depth at which magma cools, the coarser the resulting rock will be.

At times the pressure of surrounding rock forces the molten magma upward to the surface where, from the vents of volcanoes or from rifts and fissures in the earth's crust, it pours out as *lava*. Because lava is exposed to the atmosphere, it cools more rapidly than magma trapped within the crust; the extrusive rocks thus formed are therefore extremely fine in texture. Lava may even cool so rapidly that no crystallization of minerals takes place and the end product is volcanic glass.

Igneous rocks as a whole can be distinguished from sedimentary and metamorphic rocks by their texture of interlocking crystalline particles. Regardless of the direction in which the rock is viewed or broken, this texture will appear uniform throughout the entire rock.

INTRUSIVE IGNEOUS ROCKS

To the layman, **granite** is probably the best known of all intrusive rocks because of its wide use in building construction and monumental stonework. The rock itself is light in color with a uniform granular texture. Although some types of granite have a finer grain than others, the individual mineral grains are generally large enough to be identified with only a hand lens.

"True" granite is composed of about 30 percent quartz and 60 percent potash feldspars. Some plagioclase feldspar may also be present but never in amounts exceeding 5 percent. The dark grains are usually biotite mica (Plate 1), hornblende, or one of the other ferromagnesian minerals. Quartz, the gray mineral in granite, is easily recognized by its hardness and glassy luster. The color of the feldspar—which may be

Collecting on a mine dump. *Hoppock Associates*

white, gray, pink, or red—largely determines the overall color of the rock.

Granodiorite is less common than granite, but it is so similar in appearance that it is almost impossible to distinguish between the two without a microscope. The chief difference is that in granodiorite the feldspar content is mostly plagioclase, whereas in granite it is mostly potash. If anything, granodiorite may be slightly darker in color, since an increase in plagioclase is usually accompanied by some increase in ferromagnesian minerals. Granite and granodiorite grade into each other through a series of intermediate rocks.

Syenite (Figure 6) is still another light-colored intrusive that is similar to granite in texture but contains little or no quartz. Like granite, syenite is composed mainly of potash feldspars with only a small amount of plagioclase. Ferromagnesian minerals usually make up about 10 percent of the rock's bulk. Nepheline (a feldspathoid may also be present, in which case the rock is known as *nepheline syenite*. Nepheline may sometimes be mistaken for quartz because of their close resemblance, but this mineral is not as hard as quartz and has a greasy rather than a glassy luster.

FIGURE 6 Porphyritic syenite specimen from Wassau, Wisconsin. *Hoppock Associates*

Monzonite also contains little or no quartz and is very similar in appearance to syenite. Here, again, the difference is based on the ratio of plagioclase to potash feldspar. With an increase in potash feldspar, monzonite grades into syenite.

Diorite has the uniform granular texture of granite but is much darker in color due to an abundance of ferromagnesian minerals, principally hornblende. Diorite is composed mainly of plagioclase feldspar with little or no quartz or potash feldspar. Although pyroxenes are only rarely the dark constituents of diorite, some biotite mica is usually present.

Gabbro is another basic, granite-textured rock in which dark minerals predominate. Like diorite, gabbro contains little or no quartz, its composition being mainly plagioclase feldspars and pyroxenes with some olivine (Figure 7). A fine-grained gabbro is sometimes called *diabase* or *dolerite*. The Palisades which flank the lower stretches of the Hudson River are a diabase sill.

FIGURE 7 Olivine gabbro from the Wichita Mountains, Oklahoma. *Hoppock Associates*

Peridotite is a very dark crystalline rock made up almost entirely of ferromagnesian minerals; less than 5 percent of its composition is feldspar. The chief minerals in peridotite are the pyroxenes and olivine. It may also contain some hornblende. An altered variety of peridotite, called *Kimberlite* (Figure 8), is the famed, diamond-bearing "blue ground" of South Africa.

FIGURE 8 Kimberlite (Diamondiferous) from Du Toitspan Mine, Kimberly, South Africa. *Hoppock Associates*

Pegmatite is a coarsely crystalline rock, frequently associated with granite and usually similar to it in composition. It occurs most commonly as dikes or veins cutting through large bodies of plutonic rock (Figure 9). Pegmatite has an irregular grain, with crystals measuring anywhere from a fraction of an inch to several feet in length. In some localities, individual crystals of mica, quartz, and feldspar may reach abnormal size and weigh thousands of pounds. Many minerals of commercial value as well as rare minerals and gemstones are found in pegmatite. Pockets and cavities in the rock often yield large, beautifully

FIGURE 9 Small vein of pegmatite in slate. *Hoppock Associates*

formed crystals of the type so eagerly sought by collectors. *Graphic granite* (Figure 10), a variety of pegmatite, is composed of interpenetrating crystals of microline feldspar and quartz that form a strange angular pattern resembling ancient cuneiform script.

Porphyry lacks the uniform texture common to most igneous rocks. Instead it has a mixed texture of large crystals, called *phenocrysts,* imbedded in a much finer-grained groundmass. The porphyritic texture results when an igneous rock has solidified in two distinct stages. The large crystals probably develop from the molten magma first, and attain their size over a considerable period of time before the magma which forms the groundmass solidifies around them. The porphyritic texture may occur in both intrusive and extrusive rocks. Since porphyries are named for the type of rock forming the groundmass, there are many varieties, such as granite porphyry, trachyte porphyry (Figure 11), and basalt porphyry.

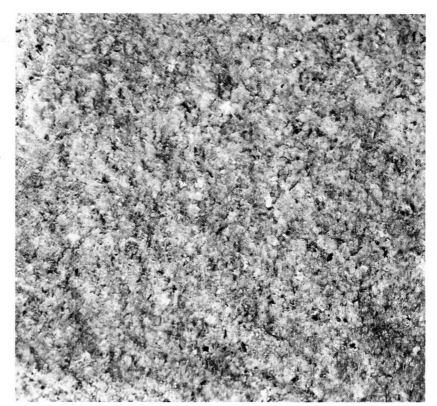

PLATE 1 Biotite granite (fine-grained), Westerly, Rhode Island. *Hoppock Associates*

PLATE 2 Obsidian, Lake County, Oregon. *Hoppock Associates*

PLATE 3 Cassiterite, Keystone, South Dakota. *Hoppock Associates*

PLATE 4 Wood replaced by chalcedony (polished section), California. *Hoppock Associates*

PLATE 5 Red sandstone,
Blairstown, New Jersey.
Hoppock Associates

PLATE 6 Wulfenite on calcite,
Chihuahua, Mexico. *Hoppock
Associates*

PLATE 7 Shale, Marksboro, New Jersey. *Hoppock Associates*

PLATE 8 Shale formation, Marksboro, New Jersey. *Hoppock Associates*

FIGURE 10 Graphic granite from Portland, Connecticut. *Hoppock Associates*

FIGURE 11 Trachyte porphyry with pink potash-feldspar phenocrysts imbedded in a finer-grained groundmass. Specimen from Brannockburn Township, Ontario, Canada. *Hoppock Associates*

Museum specimen showing pyrite vein in the zinc ore of the famed
Franklin-Ogdensburg district, New Jersey. *Hoppock Associates*

EXTRUSIVE IGNEOUS ROCKS

Felsite is a general field term applied to any of the light-colored
extrusive rocks that cannot be more accurately classified. The very fine
grain common to extrusives make positive field identification difficult,
if not impossible. For this reason rocks such as rhyolite, trachyte,
andesite, latite, and others are lumped together under the name
"felsite." Felsites may be white, buff, pale gray, pink, or reddish in color.
Some may show a parallel banding, or streaking, due to a flow structure.
All felsites have a dull fracture not unlike that of broken porcelain. A
porphyritic texture is quite common in some types, as are small gas
cavities known as *vesicles*.

FIGURE 12 Rhyolite from Castle Rock, Colorado. The apparent banding is due to the flow structure of the rock. *Hoppock Associates*

Felsites are essentially the volcanic equivalent of light-colored intrusives and have a similar composition. *Rhyolite* (Figure 12), for example, is the equivalent of granite: *trachyte* is the equivalent of syenite; *latite* of monzonite; *quartz latite* of granodiorite; and *andesite* of diorite.

Obsidian is a dark-colored natural glass of the same chemical composition as granite and rhyolite but very different from them in outward appearance. Obsidian is formed when lava cools too rapidly to allow the crystallization of minerals. Although the color of obsidian is usually black, dark brown, or very dark gray, thin slivers of the rock may be transparent and almost colorless. Occasionally it exhibits swirls of delicate rainbow colors due to an internal reflection of light. Obsidian is easily recognized by its glassy luster and a distinctive conchoidal fracture which is shown in Plate 2. A dull, partially altered form of obsidian is known as *pitchstone*. Although large quantities of obsidian are found in regions of geologically "recent" volcanic activity, it is not a common rock, and in the United States it has never been found east of the Mississippi.

Pumice (Figure 13) is a light-colored, frothy obsidian filled with myriad tiny air pockets which give the rock enough buoyancy to float readily in water. Pumice occurs in volcanic regions throughout the world and is widely used as an abrasive.

FIGURE 13 Pumice from Millard County, Utah. *Hoppock Associates*

Trap is a popular term for dense, dark-colored extrusives which, like the felsites, cannot be positively identified without a microscope. Traps are dark gray, dark green, or black, although as they weather, they usually turn a rusty brown due to the large amount of iron in their composition. For this reason, they are rarely used as building stones. Crushed traprock, however, is used extensively in the construction of roadbeds, as railroad ballast, and in the mixing of concrete. The term "trap" is also applied by quarrymen to some dark, fine-grained intrusives such as diabase.

Basalt, the volcanic equivalent of gabbro, is the most abundant of the dark-colored extrusive rocks, and the one most often referred to as "trap." Extensive flows of basaltic lava are found in many parts of the world; particularly notable are those in the Columbia River region of the northwestern United States. Numerous gas cavities, or vesicles, often form on or near the surface of a flow. These are of particular interest to collectors, since at times they are filled with agate, amethyst, or zeolite minerals. Shrinkage cracks, caused by rapid cooling, produce the five- or six-sided columnar structure which is a common characteristic of basaltic rock formations.

Sedimentary Rocks

Sedimentary rocks cover nearly three-quarters of the earth's surface, mantling a large portion of the older crystalline rocks that are the "true" crust of the earth.

Most sedimentary rocks are formed by material that has weathered or eroded from previously existing igneous or metamorphic rocks. This detrital material is then transported from its place of origin by water, ice, wind, or gravity, and deposited at some new location. The place of deposition may be only a few feet from where the sediments originated or it may be thousands of miles away. All sedimentary rocks show a more or less distinct parallel layering, or *stratification*, a feature that serves to distinguish them from other types of rocks.

Sedimentary rocks are divided into two groups: *clastic* and *nonclastic*. The clastic rocks are formed from a compacted accumulation of solid fragments that may range in size from minute, clay-size particles to boulders a foot or more in diameter. Nonclastic rocks are formed by the precipitation of dissolved mineral material as the result of various complex chemical or organic processes.

Conglomerate is essentially waterworn gravel cemented in a finer-grained matrix. The rounded pebbles making up the rock may range in size from a quarter of an inch to almost a foot in diameter. They are usually quartz, although they can be any type of rock. Sand more or less fills the spaces between the pebbles, and the whole is held together by silica or some other material that acts as a cement. The term *pudding stone* is applied to conglomerates when there is a sharp contrast between the color of the groundmass and that of the pebbles.

Breccia is similar to conglomerate but this rock is composed of angular, sharply broken rock fragments rather than worn, rounded ones. Conglomerates and breccias grade into coarse sandstones.

Sandstone (Plate 5), as its name suggests, is formed when beds of sand-sized particles are consolidated into rock. The sand, which is usually quartz, may have accumulated beneath the waters of shallow seas,

Pyrite and calcite from Santa Eulalia, Chihuahua, Mexico. *Hoppock Associates*

Chrysolite (asbestos), a variety of serpentine, from the Thetford Mines, Quebec, Canada. *Hoppock Associates*

or been deposited by rivers, or piled up in dunes by the wind. A binding material such as silica, calcite, or an iron oxide holds the sand grains tightly together. The character of the binder is largely responsible for the color of the rock as well as its resistance to weathering. Sandstone in which silica is the cementing agent is generally harder and more durable than other types and therefore better suited for use as a building stone. Sandstone may be white, buff, various shades of gray, red, or reddish brown. The red and reddish brown types contain hematite or some other iron oxide. At one time these so-called "brownstones" were widely used as facing for city houses. *Arkose* is a form of sandstone that contains considerable feldspar as well as quartz. With the addition of clay, fine-grained sandstone grades off into a sandy shale.

Shale (Plates 7 and 8) is composed of mud, clay, or silt that is so firmly compacted as to form rock. The very fine-grained sediments give the rock a smooth, uniform texture. Shale is characteristically thin-bedded or laminated, and splits easily along closely spaced layers. Similar rocks without apparent layering are more correctly called *mudstones*. Shales formed from sediments deposited in glacial lakes may show an alternate banding of light and dark layers. Each pair of layers, called a *varve,* represents an annual accumulation of silt—the lighter layer being deposited during the summer; the thinner, dark layer during the winter. By counting the number of varves, geologists are able to date and correlate glacial deposits.

Shale is usually some shade of muddy gray, although it may be yellow, brown, red, or black. With an increase in quartz, shale grades into sandstone; with the addition of calcite, it grades into limestone.

NONCLASTIC SEDIMENTARY ROCKS

Limestone is the most common of the nonclastic sedimentary rocks and one of the most important of all rocks from an economic standpoint. It is widely quarried for use as a flux in the smelting of iron, for building and construction work, and as a source of lime and cement.

Although limestone is composed primarily of a single mineral (calcite), its origin is extremely variable. Some limestone is formed by the direct chemical precipitation of calcium carbonate from water. In the case of *oolitic limestone,* the calcium carbonate is deposited, layer upon layer, around some nucleus, usually a sand grain, a bit of shell, or the skeletal remains of a tiny microorganism. When consolidated, these small, spherical concretions give the resulting rock a texture that resembles fish roe. *Tufa,* a white, cellular limestone, is precipitated from the calcium carbonate-rich waters of hot springs. *Travertine,* which is less porous than tufa and often colored by some impurity, is formed in a similar manner. Most limestone, however, is of marine origin and is the product of organic rather than chemical precipitation. Many marine organisms such as mollusks, corals, and crinoids utilize the calcium carbonate in sea water for the development of their resistant parts. As the organisms die, their shells and skeletons gradually accumulate on the sea floor, and when consolidated, they produce limestone. *Chalk,* a very soft type of limestone, is composed primarily of microscopic foraminiferal shells. The *coquina limestone,* common in Florida, consists of larger and more loosely consolidated shells and shell fragments (Figure 14). Limestone formed in ancient seas frequently contains fossils. Although the color of limestone is most often some shade

FIGURE 14 Coquina limestone from St. Augustine, Florida. *Hoppock Associates*

of gray, it may also be white, buff, tan, pink, red, bluish, or black. Limestone grades into both shale and sandstone.

Crystalline limestone is a secondary rock produced by the recrystallization of the calcium carbonate in an existing limestone. It is therefore closely related to marble, but still considered a sedimentary rather than a metamorphic rock unless it is deformed by pressure.

Under certain conditions, the calcium present in limestone may be wholly or partially replaced by magnesium. **Dolomite,** the rock that results from this replacement, is so similar to limestone that a chemical test is needed to distinguish between them. As a rule, dolomite will not effervesce readily in cold acid unless it is powdered.

FIGURE 15 Selenite gypsum from Washington County, Utah. *Hoppock Associates*

The minerals **gypsum** (Figure 15), **anhydrite,** and **halite** (rock salt) (Figure 16 and Plate 11) are also considered sedimentary rocks. They are formed by the evaporation of sea water and thus are known as *evaporites*. As salt water slowly evaporates, the minerals dissolved in it precipitate in a definite sequence according to their solubility. Gypsum, the least soluble mineral, will precipitate from solution first, anhydrite next, and halite last. These three evaporites are frequently found interlayered in extensive beds many hundreds of feet thick.

Metamorphic Rocks

Metamorphism is a geologic process by which existing sedimentary and igneous rocks are altered through the combined action of heat, pressure, and fluids. The metamorphic rocks that result from this alteration process may show little change, or they may be so drastically altered as

FIGURE 16 Halite (rock salt) from the International Salt Company Mines, Detroit, Michigan. *Hoppock Associates*

to bear little resemblance to the rocks from which they originated. Some metamorphic rocks merely exhibit a change in texture; in others, new minerals may have formed through a recombination of chemical elements. Many metamorphic rocks have a leaflike or wavy texture resulting from the parallel alignment of mica or other platy (platelike) minerals. In many others, the minerals are arranged in alternating bands or streaks.

There is reason to believe that metamorphism takes place deep within the earth's crust rather than at or near the surface. In the case of *regional metamorphism,* great masses of rock in an extensive area are usually involved. Regional metamorphism may result from crustal movements, or take place in connection with certain igneous activity. It may also occur where rock has been deeply buried beneath an excessive load of sediments.

Contact metamorphism is more localized, affecting only those rocks that are directly adjacent to an intrusive body of magma. Gases and fluids escaping from the invading magma permeate the surrounding rock, altering the existing minerals along the zone of contact and often creating a variety of new minerals.

SOME COMMON METAMORPHIC ROCKS

Marble (Plate 13) is a massive, fine- to coarse-grained rock that results from the direct alteration of limestone or dolomite. Normally white, marble is frequently colored pink, buff, green, red, brown, gray, or black by impurities. The impurities may be clumped together in patches or spread out in streaks and swirls, giving the rock its characteristic pattern. A wide variety of minerals occur in marble that has been formed from impure limestone.

Quartzite (Figure 17) is an exceedingly hard, recrystallized sandstone. It is similar to sandstone in color, and is composed of quartz grains firmly welded together by intense metamorphism. Quartzite has a granular, sugary texture. Unlike sandstone, it fractures through the quartz grains rather than around them. Fracture surfaces show a characteristic glassy sheen. Quartzite may also form from quartz conglomerates (Figure 18).

Slate (Plate 14) is a common, very fine-grained metamorphic rock, formed by the direct alteration of shale. Sometimes remnants of the rock's original bedding (layering) are still apparent. Characteristically well-foliated, or layered, slate breaks easily into broad, thin sheets which may or may not be parallel to the bedding plane. Its color is usually dark gray, but it may also be red, green, brown, or black.

Phyllite is similar in origin to slate but more highly metamorphosed. It has a coarser texture than slate, and cleavage surfaces (see page 61) show a silky luster because of the many fine grains of mica present in the rock.

Schist is more highly metamorphosed than phyllite and somewhat coarser in texture, with individual minerals distinctly visible. The min-

FIGURE 17 White quartzite from Hancock, West Virginia. *Hoppock Associates*

FIGURE 18 Quartzite, a metamorphosed quartz conglomerate from Green Pond, New Jersey. *Hoppock Associates*

erals are usually platy or rodlike in shape, with one characteristic mineral predominating. Schist is finely laminated, and when broken, yields an uneven or wavy surface. This type of separation is known as "schistosity" and serves to distinguish schist from similar metamorphic rocks. Schist may be derived from either an igneous or a sedimentary rock. Varieties are named for their most prominent mineral. The most common variety is mica schist (Figure 19), which is composed chiefly of quartz and either biotite or muscovite mica. In this rock the mica is aligned with cleavage planes roughly parallel to each other. Other varieties of schist include chlorite schist, hornblende schist, talc schist, and quartz schist.

FIGURE 19 Vishnu mica schist from the pre-Cambrian strata of the Grand Canyon, Arizona. *Hoppock Associates*

Gneiss (Figure 20) is one of the most common of the metamorphic rocks. It is extremely variable in both origin and appearance. Its general coloration ranges from white to dark gray. Quite often gneiss resembles granite but is distinguished from it by a parallel alignment of mica. The name "gneiss" (pronounced "nice") is derived from the German, and means literally "banded rock." This is probably the best description of gneiss since the light and dark minerals in the rock are segregated into alternating layers or bands. Gneiss usually contains more feldspar than schist, and its lack of "schistosity" distinguishes it from this rock. Varieties of gneiss are named for their most characteristic mineral or for the rocks from which they originated, as in the case of granite gneiss.

FIGURE 20 Biotite gneiss from Harrisville, New York. *Hoppock Associates*

Hornfels (Figure 21) is a product of contact metamorphism. It results from the action of intense heat on "country rock" (usually shale), in a zone directly adjacent to an invading body of magma. It is, in fact, found as a sheathing around almost all igneous instrusions. The rock itself is hard, dense, and unfoliated, with the general appearance of baked clay. Hornfels is usually dark in color and often spotted by larger crystals. When broken, it yields a curved fracture surface.

FIGURE 21 Corderite hornfels specimen from Butte, Montana. *Hoppock Associates*

Examining Rocks

Although descriptions and photographs are helpful, the best way to learn about rocks is to see the actual rocks themselves, and whenever possible, to examine them closely with a hand lens.

Rocks are not hard to find. Once the collector becomes "rock conscious," he should have little trouble locating specimens to study. In fact, he will probably find some of the rocks described in this chapter in his own backyard or neighborhood. Ridges, cliffs, slopes, bluffs, and other natural outcrops of rock can be found in cities as well as in rural areas. Quite often rocks such as basalt and granite form outcrops that are so distinctive in appearance that it is possible to identify these rocks even from a considerable distance. Bare rock is frequently exposed in excavations for new buildings, or along streets, highways, and railroad right-of-ways.

The collector should note particularly the various kinds of rocks found in the area in which he lives or where he plans to do the major portion of his mineral collecting. If possible, he should collect representative examples of these rocks. In this way he can study them more closely at his leisure and at the same time gain some practice in using a geologist's hammer. A hand magnifier will reveal much about the structure and composition of rocks that cannot be seen with the unaided eye. In some rocks even the individual minerals can be accurately identified in this manner.

Collectors sometimes find a small study collection of common rocks and rock-forming minerals useful in identifying unknown rocks. Inexpensive study collections can usually be purchased from mineral dealers or scientific supply houses. The specimens in such a collection need not be large, but they should be characteristic.

Minerals | 3

While a rock is usually an aggregate of minerals, a mineral is a distinct homogeneous substance with definite physical and chemical properties. Because these properties are constant or vary only within certain fixed limits, they serve to distinguish one mineral species from another. Many minerals can be identified solely by properties that can be observed or determined by simple tests. There are, of course, others that cannot be identified so easily, and even the most experienced collector must at times seek the advice and help of a museum curator or a professional mineralogist. The mineral properties that will be most useful to the beginner in identifying specimens will be described later; but, first, a word about the composition and structure of minerals.

What Is a Mineral?

A mineral is composed of one or more of the natural chemical elements. About twenty minerals are *native* (uncombined) elements, and can be divided into *metals, semimetals,* and *nonmetals.* The native metals include such elements as gold, silver, copper (Figure 22), lead, mercury, platinum, and iron. The native semimetals include arsenic, antimony, bismuth, tellurium, and selenium. The native nonmetals are sulfur,

FIGURE 22 Native copper from Calumet, Michigan. *Hoppock Associates*

diamond (Figure 23), and graphite. Good specimens of many native elements are rare, and thus seldom seen in the average collection.

All minerals other than the native elements consist of two or more elements which have been united chemically in a *compound* by various natural inorganic processes. The composition of a mineral can be expressed by means of a chemical formula. In a formula of this type, elements are represented by one or two letter symbols derived from their English or Latin names. The proportions of each element present in the compound are indicated by numerals. For example, the formula for quartz is SiO_2 which tells at a glance that this mineral consists of silicon (Si) and oxygen (O) atoms in the ratio of 1:2.

On the basis of chemical composition, minerals are divided into twelve *classes:* (1) Elements; (2) Sulfides; (3) Sulfosalts; (4) Oxides; (5) Halides; (6) Carbonates; (7) Nitrates; (8) Borates; (9) Phosphates; (10) Sulfates; (11) Tungstates; (12) Silicates. These chemical classes are subdivided into *families* which, in turn, are subdivided into *groups*. A

FIGURE 23 Doubly terminated "Herkimer Diamond" (rock crystal) in matrix. Specimen from Herkimer County, New York. *Hoppock Associates*

group is made up of species which may, or may not, have several *varieties*. This scheme of mineral classification, based on the Dana system*, is the one most widely used by collectors as well as professional mineralogists.

Crystals

A true mineral is said to be crystalline because it has a unique internal structure of atoms or ions packed together in a symmetrical, three-dimensional pattern. The few exceptions that are noncrystalline are called *mineraloids*. A mineraloid does not have an orderly internal structure and thus is *amorphous* (formless). Opal is a good example of a mineraloid. Under favorable conditions most crystalline minerals assume outward forms known as crystals. Crystals are regular, geometric

*C. Palache, H. Berman, and C. Frondel, *Dana's System of Mineralogy*, 7th ed., 3 Vols. (New York: John Wiley and Sons, 1944–62). The finest and most authoritative compilation of mineral data in the English language.

solids having smooth, plane surfaces or *faces*. Since the external crystal form reflects the internal atomic structure of the mineral, crystals can be important in mineral identification.

All crystals can be divided into six main groups, or *crystal systems*, according to the number, position, and relative lengths of their axes. A *crystallographic axis* is an imaginary line of reference that extends through the center of a crystal and is parallel to the intersecting edges of its main faces. All crystals have three crystallographic axes, except those belonging to the hexagonal system, which have four. The six crystal systems are:

Isometric (Cubic) System: includes crystals with three axes of equal length at right angles to one another. Examples: galena, pyrite, halite.

Tetragonal System: includes crystals having three axes perpendicular to one another; two horizontal axes of equal length; and a shorter or longer vertical axis. Examples: zircon, scheelite, cassiterite.

Hexagonal System: includes crystals with three horizontal axes of equal length intersecting at angles of 120 degrees; a longer or shorter vertical axis is perpendicular to these. Examples: beryl, tourmaline (Figure 28), calcite (Figure 24), quartz (Figure 25).

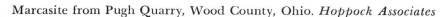

Marcasite from Pugh Quarry, Wood County, Ohio. *Hoppock Associates*

FIGURE 24 Brown, scalenohedral crystals of calcite from Chihuahua, Mexico. *Hoppock Associates*

FIGURE 25 A tiny quartz crystal grows from the face of a larger crystal. Specimen from Hot Springs, Arkansas. *Hoppock Associates*

Orthorhombic System: includes crystals with three mutually perpendicular axes of unequal length. Examples: sulfur, barite, topaz.

Monoclinic System: includes crystals with three unequal axes, two of which are at an oblique angle, with the third perpendicular to the plane of the other two. Examples: gypsum (Figure 26), mica, orthoclase.

Triclinic System: includes crystals having three unequal axes, none of which forms a right angle with any other. Examples: plagioclase, microcline, albite.

FIGURE 26 These bladed crystals of gypsum (selenite) include much sand. This specimen comes from the Great Salt Plain, Jet, Oklahoma. *Hoppock Associates*

These six crystal systems can be subdivided into thirty-two *classes,* or *point groups,* of which only about fifteen are of importance to the mineral collector.

Although crystals occur in numerous *forms,* there are certain basic forms that are characteristic of each of the six crystal systems. The cube, octahedron, and dodecahedron are basic forms belonging to the isometric system. In crystallography, the term *form* is used in a restricted sense to denote all like faces on a crystal. The six square faces of a cube, being alike, constitute a form. Sometimes a crystal has only one form, but more often it shows a combination of several forms. A crystal, however, can never show forms other than those of its own crystal system.

The occurrence of perfectly formed crystals in nature is rare but, when found, they are highly prized by collectors. Crystals showing well-formed faces on all sides are termed *euhedral.* Those on which the faces are imperfectly or partially developed are *subhedral.* Lacking faces entirely, a crystalline mineral is said to be *anhedral.* Crystals seldom grow at the same rate in all directions, which is perhaps the main reason why so many show unequal face development. Nearly all natural crystals have some type of internal or external imperfection. Close examination with a hand lens usually reveals minute grooves, ridges, and mottlings on crystal faces that otherwise appear smooth and flawless. Crystals of certain minerals frequently show such irregularities as overgrowths, offsets, striations (Figure 27), phantom inner crystals, and inclusions of another mineral. At times these so-called "imperfections" add greatly to the beauty and/or value of specimens.

FIGURE 27 Black tourmaline crystal showing characteristic striations. Specimen from Minas Gerais, Brazil. *Hoppock Associates*

The *twinning*, or pairing, of crystals is a common phenomenon that results from an intergrowth of two or more crystals at a specific angle. Twinned crystals can be of either a *contact* or a *penetration* type. The surfaces of contact crystals adhere to one another while the penetration-type crystals grow out of or through one another. In some minerals—staurolite, for example—twinning is so frequent and distinctive that it is a valuable means of identification.

When the chemical composition of a mineral is altered by replacement or weathering, but its crystal form remains unchanged, it is known as a *pseudomorph*. A pseudomorph can be extremely deceptive, since it is essentially a mineral having the crystal form of another mineral species. Common pseudomorphs are limonite after pyrite, and chlorite after garnet.

A *paramorph*, like a pseudomorph, is derived from another mineral and still retains its crystal form. However, paramorphism results from a rearrangement of a mineral's atomic structure, rather than from a

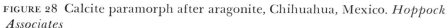

FIGURE 28 Calcite paramorph after aragonite, Chihuahua, Mexico. *Hoppock Associates*

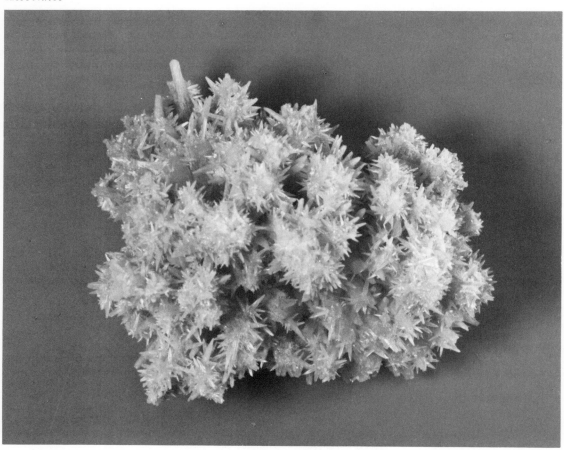

change in its chemical composition. Calcite, being similar in composition, is frequently a paramorph after aragonite (Figure 28).

Habits of Minerals

The term *habit* is used in mineralogy to denote the outward appearance of a mineral, including its general shape and crystal form or combination of forms. Various other terms are used to describe the characteristic habits of minerals and crystals, including the following:

Acicular—needlelike

Amygdaloidal—almond-shaped

Arborescent—branching, treelike

Bladed—elongated and flattened like a knife blade

Botryoidal—rounded, resembling a bunch of grapes

Capillary—hairlike

Columnar—shaped like a column

Dendritic—branched, somewhat plantlike

Drusy—coated with numerous minute crystals

Felted—closely matted

Fibrous—threadlike

Filiform—in twisted and matted threads

Foliated—in thin, easily separated, leaflike layers

Granular—an aggregate of grains

Lamellar—in thin, flat scales or plates

Mammillary—large, rounded, breastlike

Massive—having no particular form or shape

Micaceous—in thin, easily separated sheets

Oolitic—in small, spherical grains resembling fish roe

Pisolitic—in spherical grains about the size of peas

Prismatic—elongated, pencil-shaped

Radiated—diverging from a common center

Reniform—kidney-shaped

Reticulated—netted, a network of crystals

Stellated—starlike clusters, or groups, of crystals

Tabular—in flat plates but thicker than lamellar

Identifying Mineral Specimens

A single physical or chemical property seldom provides enough evidence to positively identify a mineral. Identification is therefore based on a series of observations and tests, most of which are simple enough to be performed in the field. Extensive chemical testing is rarely needed, and most collectors rely almost entirely on physical tests to identify specimens. The few chemical tests that collectors find useful require little in the way of chemicals and equpiment but are best made in the home lab. Some of these tests are described in Chapter 5.

A mineral specimen that is to be identified should first be examined visually in a good, strong light. A hand magnifier will help to bring out small, but often important, details that might otherwise be overlooked. The color, luster, and diaphaneity of the specimen should be noted and written down. Fracture surfaces and cleavage planes should also be noted. Crystals should be classified as to form and habit. Any irregularities, striations, inclusions, and etch marks should be carefully observed and recorded. Tests for such physical properties as hardness, tenacity, streak, and magnetism can then be made, and the specific gravity of the specimen approximated by the "heft" method. Any other species found in association with the specimen should be particularly noted, and whenever possible, the matrix identified. The data obtained from these tests and observations can then be used in conjunction with determinative tables to identify the specimen, or at least to narrow the possibilities down to a few species. In the event that the mineral's identity is still questionable, a few simple chemical tests may be called for.

Skill in identifying minerals increases with practice. The more often a collector sees a particular mineral, the easier it will be for him to recognize it again. For this reason a beginner should visit museums that have mineral collections, and look at labeled specimens as often as possible.

Physical Properties of Minerals

Color can be directly related to the composition of a mineral or it can be the result of some minor impurity. In the case of native metals and most minerals having a metallic luster, color is a constant property, and unless masked by tarnish, it is an important means of identification. Other minerals, particularly transparent and translucent ones, may show considerable variation in color. Some may even exhibit a gradation of colors, or have colors arranged in zones or bands. Occasionally, as in smoky quartz, the mineral's original color has been altered by the presence of radioactive minerals in the surrounding rocks. Although color can be an important property, it is not inherent in all minerals; many are colorless or white. For purposes of identification, color is best used only in conjunction with more reliable clues. Whenever possible, it should be observed on a freshly broken rather than on a weathered surface.

Though the color of a particular mineral may vary widely from one specimen to another, its *streak* remains constant. Streak refers to the color of a mineral when it has been ground to a fine powder. In powder form, many minerals lose their color or turn a lighter tint of their original color. There are some minerals, however, that show a brighter or entirely different color which is useful in identifying them. For convenience, most collectors determine the streak of a mineral by rubbing a piece of it across a streak plate (Plate 15), which is nothing more than an ordinary unglazed white tile. A streak plate cannot be used for testing minerals whose hardness is greater than 7 (see page 63).

Luster refers to the manner in which light is reflected from the surface of a mineral. It can be divided into two types: *metallic* and *nonmetallic*. A metallic luster needs little description, since everyone is familiar with the typical surface appearance of a metal such as gold, copper, or lead. The term *submetallic* is sometimes used to describe a luster that is almost, but not quite, metallic. *Adamantine, vitreous, pearly, silky, greasy,* and *resinous* are the various terms applied to lusters that are nonmetallic. *Adamantine* describes a luster which is hard and brilliant like that of a diamond. *Vitreous* refers to the glasslike luster of minerals such as quartz and hornblende. A *pearly* luster is frequently shown by platy minerals and may also be observed on the cleavage surfaces (see below) of many others. Because of their finely fibrous structure, serpentine and satin-spar gypsum can be said to have *silky* lusters. A *resinous* (rosinlike) luster is less common, but is seen in sulfur and specimens of sphalerite. The slightly oily appearance of nepheline is typical of minerals having a *greasy* luster. Minerals with no apparent luster are referred to as *dull* or *earthy*.

The ability of some minerals to transmit light is called **diaphaneity**. The terms *transparent, translucent,* and *opaque* indicate the degree to which a mineral possesses this property. When a mineral is *translucent,* it transmits light freely and the outline of an object viewed through the mineral is clearly discernable. A *translucent* mineral is capable of transmitting light, but an object cannot be seen through it. An *opaque* mineral transmits no light even on its thinnest edges. Sometimes a black or dark-colored mineral appears opaque but a thin sliver will soon reveal its ability to transmit some light.

Cleavage is a property peculiar to some minerals, but not to all of them. Those minerals that show cleavage will, under the proper stress, break smoothly along natural planes of weakness which are directly related to their internal atomic structure. Cleavage is directional and always occurs along planes that are parallel to possible crystal faces. The quality of cleavage is described as *eminent* (mica), *perfect* (fluorite), *good, fair,* and *poor* (bornite). Quality refers to the relative flatness and smoothness of the cleavage surfaces. Cleavage may be in one, two, three, four, or six directions, and is usually described as *cubic, octahedral, rhombohedral, prismatic,* or *pinacoidal,* depending on which of these forms the cleavage parallels.

Many minerals break in random directions rather than along well-defined cleavage planes. This manner of breaking, or *fracture,* produces a characteristic surface, the nature of which may be useful in identifying a mineral. If the broken surface is fairly smooth, the fracture of the mineral is said to be *even*; if rough, the fracture is *uneven* or *irregular*. A *fibrous* or *splintery* fracture resembles the break in wood; a *hackly* fracture has the jagged appearance of torn metal; and an *earthy* fracture is crumbly like soil or clay. A curving, shell-like fracture is termed *conchoidal,* and is most notable in noncrystalline substances such as opal and obsidian (Plate 2).

Tenacity is the resistance of a mineral to being broken and should not be confused with "hardness," which is an entirely different property. A mineral is *brittle* if a sliver or small sample breaks or powders easily when it is snapped between the fingers or tapped lightly with a hammer. Though the majority of minerals possess this kind of tenacity, some minerals are *elastic* or *flexible*. When bent, an elastic mineral such as mica does not break and resumes its original position as soon as the pressure is released. A flexible mineral also bends without breaking, but it remains deformed after the release of pressure. Metals are characteristically *malleable*; that is, they can be hammered or flattened into thin sheets without crumbling. Metals such as silver and copper are also *ductile* (though this cannot be determined by a simple field test), and thus they can be drawn into wire. A few minerals are said to be *sectile,* which means it is possible to shave them into slivers with a knife.

Hardness is the resistance that a smooth surface of a mineral offers to being scratched, and in descriptive mineralogy this property is designated by **H**. A scale of hardness, devised in 1822 by the mineralogist Friedrich Mohs, is still used as the standard for determining the relative hardness of minerals.

1. Talc
2. Gypsum
3. Calcite (cleavage faces)
4. Fluorite
5. Apatite

6. Feldspar
7. Quartz
8. Topaz
9. Corundum
10. Diamond

The minerals that comprise Mohs' scale are numbered in order of their increasing hardness; thus talc (1) is the softest mineral, and diamond (10) the hardest. The numbers do not represent the exact hardness of these minerals but rather indicate that any mineral in the scale is capable of scratching all those of a lower number, and can, in turn, be scratched by all those of a higher number. Known as *hardness points,* small chips of these minerals (excluding diamond) can be used to determine the relative hardness of a mineral when its identity is unknown. The collector can assemble a set of hardness points himself or purchase one from a mineral dealer (Figure 29). Sets of professional points are also available and consist of pointed mineral fragments mounted at the ends of brass rods. These are used primarily to determine hardnesses of 5 through 10, and include diamond.

FIGURE 29 A set of hardness points. *Hoppock Associates*

Finding the hardness of an unknown mineral is merely a case of determining which of the hardness minerals will or will not scratch the specimen. If, for instance, the specimen is scratched by fluorite (4), and can itself scratch calcite (3) the relative hardness of the specimen would be 3½.

In lieu of hardness points, the following common objects can be used:

> H 2½—Fingernail
> H 3 —Copper coin
> H 3½—Brass pin
> H 5½—Window glass
> H 5½—Penknife (good-quality steel blade)
> H 6½—Steel file

It is often useful to remember that minerals harder than 5½ will scratch glass, while those under 5½ can be scratched by a steel knife blade.

Hardness determinations should be made on a freshly broken surface, preferably in a spot where they do not show. When they are indiscriminately placed, test scratches can easily ruin the appearance and value of a specimen.

After a specimen has been tested for hardness, the test scratches should be inspected with a hand lens to be sure that they actually "bit" into the surface and are not just temporary streaks left by the softer mineral. It is wise to make test scratches in several directions, since in some minerals hardness is notably directional. The hardness of calcite, for example, is 3 on a cleavage rhombohedron, yet only 2 on the basal plane. Kyanite and phosgenite also show a pronounced difference in hardness between cleavage planes.

Magnetism is a property found in only two common minerals, magnetite (Figure 30) and pyrrhotite, which can be attracted to the poles of an ordinary pocket magnet. Platinum and native iron are also magnetic, but these minerals are extremely rare. A small alnico magnet serves to distinguish magnetite and pyrrhotite from other similar species.

In handling various minerals, the collector soon notes that some are heavier or lighter than others, even when specimens are of about equal size. This apparent difference in weight between mineral species results from a difference in specific gravity.

Specific gravity (density) is an important property of minerals and one that can be useful in identifying them. The specific gravity of a min-

PLATE 9 Torbernite, Sonora, Mexico. *Hoppock Associates*

PLATE 10 Erythrite (cobalt "bloom"), Timiskaming District, Ontario, Canada. *Hoppock Associates*

PLATE 11 Halite (rock salt),
International Salt Company
Mines, Detroit, Michigan.
Hoppock Associates

PLATE 12 Vivianite, Bingham,
Utah. *Hoppock Associates*

PLATE 13 Pink Marble, Tate, Georgia. *Hoppock Associates*

PLATE 14 Slate Formation, Marksboro, New Jersey. *Hoppock Associates*

PLATE 15 Using a streak plate.
Hoppock Associates

PLATE 16 Concretions,
Logansville, New Jersey.
Hoppock Associates

FIGURE 30 Magnetite (lodestone) is not only magnetic but also a natural magnet itself. Specimen from Magnet Cove, Arkansas. *Hoppock Associates*

eral designated by **G** is essentially the ratio between the weight of the mineral and the weight of an equal volume of water. Though it is possible for a professional mineralogist using a Jolly balance, heavy liquids, or a pycnometer to determine specific gravity with great accuracy, an approximate determination is usually sufficient for the needs of the amateur. In the home lab, specific gravity can be determined by suspending a small sample of a mineral from a spring scale by means of a string or heavy thread. The sample is first weighed in air; then, still suspended by the string, it is lowered into a beaker or jar of water, and weighed again. The weight of the sample in air, is subtracted from its weight in water to get a third figure which represents the weight of the displaced water. The specific gravity of the mineral can then be found by dividing the weight of the mineral in air by the weight of the displaced water. It is important that the mineral sample being tested be relatively pure and free of cracks.

In the field, specific gravity is usually approximated by hefting a specimen in the hand, and judging its weight in relation to the average weight of a metallic or nonmetallic mineral. The average metallic mineral has a specific gravity of slightly over 5. Thus any metallic mineral with a specific gravity less than 4 will feel light in the hand; one with a specific gravity of 6 or more will feel heavy. The average nonmetallic mineral has a specific gravity ranging between 2½ and 3; and here, again, even a small difference in specific gravity will be apparent when a specimen is hefted. An unknown specimen should be classified as light, average, or heavy. The more minerals the collector handles, the easier it will be for him to judge specific gravity in this manner.

In The Field | 4

Almost any field trip will be more successful if it is carefully planned in advance. In this way, time that could be spent collecting specimens will not be wasted in searching for the exact location of a collecting site, or in returning home for some necessary piece of equipment that was left behind.

Find out as much as possible about the collecting area to be visited before setting out on a trip. If it is not too far away, a preliminary scouting trip may prove worthwhile. Detailed directions for reaching the area should be obtained in advance of the actual trip, as well as up-to-date road and regional maps. Try to get a topographic map of the area, since it is important to know something of the terrain, particularly when a trip involves hiking or camping. A knowledge of the area's geology and the nature of its mineral deposits is also important. In the event that the area can be scouted in advance, representative samples of its rocks should be brought back for study.

Field Equipment

Make a list of the things to be taken on a field trip; then, as each item is packed, check it off against the list so that nothing is forgotten. Besides the necessary collecting and prospecting equipment (see pages 17–20),

Bauxite, the principal ore of aluminum, from Bauxite, Arkansas. *Hoppock Associates*

certain additional items may also be needed. Food is usually required even on short, one-day trips; on longer camping trips, you'll need cooking utensils as well as a camp stove and fuel. If firewood is readily available in the camping area, a single-bitted ax can be substituted for the stove and fuel. A can opener and matches are essentials too often forgotten by novice campers. Matches should be waterproof so that they can be relied on to light even in a downpour. A flashlight is useful not only for examining small pockets and crevices in rocks, but also for guiding the footsteps should darkness overtake the collector on his return to the car or base camp.

On short trips, an adequate supply of drinking water can usually be carried in canteens; on camping trips, the amount of water needed for drinking, cooking, and washing purposes, as well as the way it is supplied, will depend largely on the number of people in the party, the mode of transportation, and the area visited. These same factors will also influence the type of shelter and bedding to be used. Some people require more "creature comforts" than others and this, too, must be considered when planning a field trip. If the collector has had little or no previous camping experience, he will find more detailed information in some of the excellent books on camping that are currently available.

Clothing

The type of clothing worn on a collecting trip will depend a great deal on the climate and the season of the year. Rugged, work-type clothes made of heavy cotton denim, which are available in sizes to fit both men and women, are particularly good. They are inexpensive and have the added advantage of being washable. Even in summer, long sleeves are best since they protect the arms from sunburn, insect bites, and bramble scratches. Several lighter layers of clothing will keep the body warmer in winter than one heavy layer. Always carry along an extra sweater; if it is not needed, it can be used to cushion specimens in the collecting bag. Rainwear of some type is important, especially on a camping trip. All-leather, laced boots of a medium height are the most suitable footwear for field work and hiking. It is essential that the boots be properly fitted and large enough to be worn comfortably with two pairs of socks. Heavy wool socks are usually worn over a pair of lightweight wool or cotton socks. These serve to cushion the feet when walking and to absorb perspiration in hot weather. Some sort of hat or neckerchief should be worn to protect the head if work is to be done in the full sun. In desert country, a broad-brimmed hat or pith helmet is a necessity, regardless of the season. Most collectors wear leather or canvas gloves to protect their hands from cuts, blisters, and misdirected hammerblows.

Safety in the Field

For reasons of saftey, field trips to remote areas should never be taken alone. Collecting minerals even at some local site will be safer and more enjoyable when done in the company of fellow collectors or with member's of one's own family. In the event of illness or injury, a companion can administer first aid or go for help if it is needed. Serious personal injuries rarely happen in the field when the collector uses reasonable care and common sense. There are, however, certain sites which should be avoided because they are potentially dangerous. Old, abandoned mines, for example, are particularly hazardous and should

Pale green prenite from the Prospect Park Quarry, Paterson, New Jersey. *Hoppock Associates*

Fossil brachipods in sandstone from Basking Ridge, New Jersey. *Hoppock Associates*

never be explored except in the company of a responsible person who is familiar with the layout and the conditions that exist inside. Too often the timbers in old mines are badly rotted, and there is the imminent danger of cave-ins or the collapse of tunnel walls. Flooded shafts, poor ventilation, and the possibility of becoming lost are other good reasons for staying out of such places. Caves and abandoned "glory holes" should also be bypassed.

A well-equipped first-aid kit should always be taken on a camping trip; on local, one-day outings, the collector will be wise to carry at least a generous supply of band-aids. Since snakes have a particular fondness for rocky places, a snake-bite kit should be carried on all field trips regardless of their length. Poisonous snakes are found in every state, except Alaska and Hawaii; they are also found throughout Mexico and in some parts of southern Canada. Though very few people die from snake bites, a bite is nevertheless serious and something that requires immediate attention. Pocket-sized kits for treating snake bites are inexpensive and available at any drugstore.

Permissions

When collecting minerals on private property, be sure to get the owner's permission and make arrangements in advance whenever possible. Collecting on private property is a privilege that is often abused. The collector should make every effort to see that campfires are doused, fence gates closed, and all rubbish cleaned up before he leaves. Many property owners understandably charge a small fee for collecting privileges, and in some instances, advertise their localities in magazines devoted to mineral hobbies.

For legal reasons, most owners of operating mines and quarries do not grant collecting privileges to individuals; however, some do allow limited collecting by mineral clubs and other organized groups.

Strict laws prohibit the collecting of minerals in national parks or in other areas under the administration of the National Park Service. As a general rule, collecting is also prohibited in most state and local parks. A few states have laws forbidding the removal of fossils from local sites.

Where to Find Minerals

Many beginners make their first field trips to well-known collecting sites that are regularly visited by collectors and where they know certain

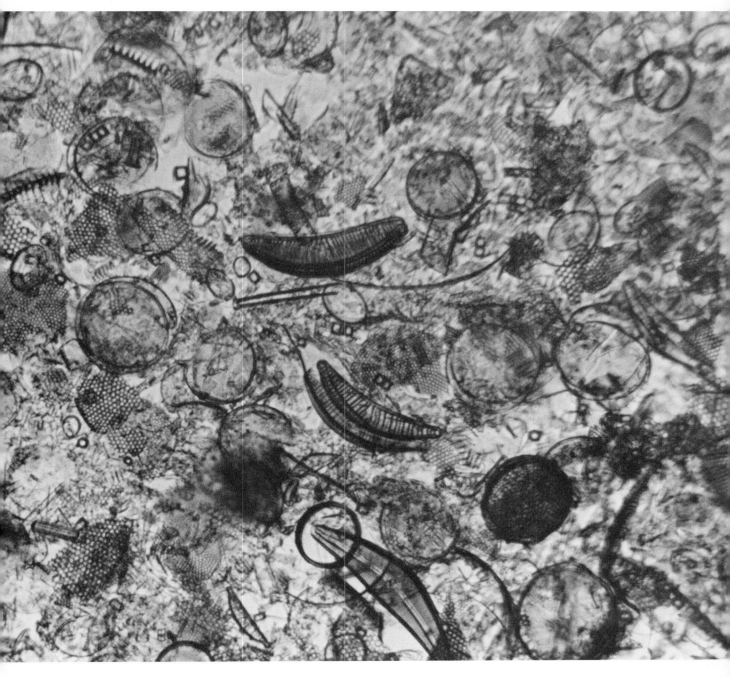

Diatomite, a variety of opal also known as diatomaceous earth, magnified to show the siliceous shells of fossil diatoms of which this mineral is formed. *Hoppock Associates*

minerals may be found. There are a great many of these sites, and chances are that the collector will find at least one or two of them located somewhere in the state or area in which he lives. Many regional guidebooks are available that list notable collecting localities and give specific directions for reaching them. Collecting sites operated as commercial or semicommercial ventures are regularly advertised in the mineral hobby magazines. These magazines often feature articles on new or interesting sites, and for this reason alone they are well worth subscribing to.

The collector who has learned to recognize the more common rocks that he encounters in the field is in a good position to search for new mineral deposits and to discover his own collecting sites. Experience will teach him that certain minerals or groups of minerals are most likely to occur in certain rocks. He will also learn that certain minerals, because they are of similar origin, are frequently found in association with each other. Miners and professional prospectors have long relied on a knowledge of these rock-mineral associations to aid them in locating valuable ore and mineral deposits. The collector, too, will find this knowledge useful. A good textbook of mineralogy generally includes information on some of the more common rock-mineral associations and usually notes as well, under descriptions of individual species, the type of rock or environment in which the mineral most often occurs.

A number of mineral environments likely to yield good specimens are particularly worthy of the collector's attention. These include pegmatites, pillow and amygdaloidal basalts, quartz vein cavities, sulfide veins, and certain eluvial and alluvial deposits. In the field, the collector should also watch for "contacts"—places where one type of rock ends and another entirely different type begins. Because minerals tend to concentrate at or near contact surfaces, these are excellent places to look for specimens.

Field Notes

As specimens are collected on a field trip, the exact locality and type of deposit from which they were taken should be recorded in a notebook reserved for this purpose. A small patch of adhesive tape should be numbered and placed on each specimen to temporarily identify it. These numbers should also be recorded in the notebook, along with any additional information that the collector believes useful. Good field notes are important, particularly when the collector plans to return to the same site at some later date.

Great care should be taken in packing mineral specimens for the return home. Examine all specimens before they are packed and discard any inferior ones. Large pieces of worthless matrix should be trimmed from specimens at this time in order to lighten the load that must be carried. If there are too many specimens for one load, several trips to the car will have to be made; or the extra specimens will have to be hidden and picked up at some later time.

Ordinary newspaper makes excellent wrapping material for minerals. An ample supply weighs very little and can be carried easily in the collecting bag.

Massive mineral material rarely needs wrapping except to prevent it from rubbing against other specimens in the collecting bag. Crystal groups and more delicate specimens should be wrapped securely in several sheets of crumpled or slightly dampened paper. Some collectors use Kleenex or toilet tissue as well as the newspaper for wrapping fragile specimens.

Wads of crumpled paper should be stuffed between the wrapped specimens as they are packed in the collecting bag. It is important that the bag be tightly packed so that its contents will not shift when it is carried. Overpacking, however, should be avoided. If tools must be carried in the bag on the return trip, it is a good idea to wrap them in newspaper as well.

At Home | 5

On returning from a collecting trip, the specimens brought home should be carefully sorted. Most specimens will require some sort of cleaning; some may also require trimming; and there will be those, perhaps, that need further identification by chemical tests. Sometimes even the minerals purchased from a dealer will need cleaning and trimming and, if present, matrix and associate minerals will have to be identified. All specimens should, of course, be properly labeled and cataloged before they are placed in the permanent collection.

Cleaning Specimens

Before attempting to clean specimens, the beginner should first acquaint himself with those minerals that cannot be washed in ordinary tap water. Such information can be obtained easily from the table of mineral solubilities that is included in most text and reference books on mineralogy. Halite and many of the sulfide, clay, and boron minerals are decomposed or seriously altered by water. In addition, there are certain other minerals, such as millerite, that cannot be washed because of their extremely delicate capillary structure.

Minerals that are insoluble in water can be washed with a garden hose or a kitchen spray, or gently sloshed up and down in a bucket of water. Great care should be taken in washing crystallized specimens so as not to break off small crystals or scar crystal faces. Deeply soiled specimens can be washed in mild soapy water and then scrubbed lightly with a vegetable brush or cellulose sponge. Minerals should never be soaked in water for prolonged periods of time or washed with strong alkali soaps or industrial detergents. Hardened clay is best removed from small cracks and crevices before a specimen is washed, since clay is inclined to swell once it is wet. Bamboo splints, toothpicks, or bent wires are good for breaking up and dislodging dry clay. Dental picks and razor blades can also be used for this purpose, provided the specimen is hard enough to resist scratching with steel blades. After their washing, specimens should be thoroughly rinsed in clean water and dried with a soft cloth. More delicate specimens can be laid in the sun to dry.

Some water-soluble minerals can be wiped clean with alcohol or carbon tetrachloride, but this treatment should never be attempted without first consulting a solubility table. Because sulphides tarnish readily, they should never be moistened with chemicals or water. Brushing with a fiber or quill brush is probably the most satisfactory method of cleaning them. Clay minerals, too, are best cleaned in this manner.

After an initial cleaning, some specimens may require additional cleaning or the removal of disfiguring rustlike stains. However, frequent or excessive cleaning with strong acids should be avoided since it may cause physical or chemical changes in a specimen or destroy its mineralogical value.

Removing Rust Stains

The unsightly yellow or reddish-brown stains caused by iron oxides can be removed from specimens or considerably lightened with oxalic acid. This acid, however, cannot be applied to carbonates or other acid soluble minerals. Oxalic acid is available in dry, crystal form at most hardware or paint stores. One half ounce of the crystals dissolved in a gallon of water will make a solution suitable for cleaning minerals.

The stained specimen should be placed in an aluminum pot reserved for this purpose, and enough acid solution should be added to cover the specimen completely. Place the pot on a stove or hot plate and allow the solution to simmer slowly for half an hour. Leave the specimen in the solution until it is cool enough to handle. It should then be washed in soapy water and rinsed several times to remove all traces of the acid. Heavily stained minerals may require several treatments.

A large nodule of flint, a variety of chalcedony, from Waterloo, New Jersey. *Hoppock Associates*

The oxalic-acid solution can also be used to remove surface tarnish from pyrite. However, frequent cleaning with acid may cause pyrite specimens to decompose or disintegrate. After being treated, pyrite should be coated with a clear lacquer to prevent more oxide from forming.

Trimming Specimens

Mineral specimens quite often need trimming to improve their proportions, and to make them easier to store or display. Although special machines are available for this purpose, they are understandably expensive, and the average amateur must rely on hammers, chisels, and other hand tools to do the job.

Ideally, a mineral specimen should be nearly square or rectangular in outline; but these proportions are sometimes difficult, if not impossible, to achieve by trimming. The character of the matrix largely determines the manner and direction in which a specimen can be split or broken. Before trimming is attempted, study each specimen, paying particular attention to the structure or grain of the matrix rock. Any pre-existing cracks along which separations might occur should be carefully noted. When there is the possibility that trimming might divide the specimen through a group of crystals or some other interesting feature, it is better to leave it in its original state.

When trimming is feasible, good results can be obtained, provided the hammers, chisels, and gads used for the job are about the same weight as the specimen. Tools that are too light will be ineffectual, whereas those that are too heavy may shatter the specimen. After a specimen has been trimmed to size, proportionately lighter tools should be used for chipping off small projections and for general shaping purposes.

Safety goggles are a "must" and should always be worn during trimming operations. Heavy leather or canvas gloves are also needed to protect the hands.

The specimen being trimmed can be held firmly in one hand or supported by sandbags, but it should never rest on a hard, rigid surface such as a rock or anvil. Soft lead blocks of the type used in art metalwork make good supports. Excess matrix should be broken off with a quick, sharp blow of the hammer rather than by a series of lighter blows. There is a certain knack to doing this, and the beginner would do well to practice on a few rocks before attempting to trim a choice specimen. Chisels and gads are of little use in breaking solid rock but they are excellent for splitting specimens along pre-existing cracks. When trimming, take care not to mar the face of the specimen since ugly tool marks are almost impossible to remove.

Laboratory Tests

When the identity of a specimen remains in doubt after it has been carefully examined and its various physical properties have been noted, certain simple chemical tests will often make positive identification possible. It is usually more practical to perform these tests at home rather than in the field, since most of them require some source of heat, as well

Chert (hornstone), a light-colored impure flint, from Joplin, Missouri. *Hoppock Associates*

as the use of acids and other chemicals. The home lab need not be elaborate; in fact, for most collectors it is a temporary setup utilizing a corner of the kitchen, attic, or basement. The basic equipment can be ordered from a scientific or chemical supply company. Some mineral dealers also stock basic test equipment. The following items are essential:

> Heat source (alcohol lamp, Bunsen burner, or candle)
> Blowpipe
> Charcoal blocks
> Test tubes (Pyrex)
> Glass tubing ($\frac{1}{4}$ inch and $\frac{3}{16}$ inch diameter)
> Chemist's forceps
> Wire test-tube holder
> Mortar and pestle

Platinum wire (27-gauge in glass holder)
Flame analyzer (Cobalt-blue glass filter)

Asbestos pad
Litmus paper

Sulphuric acid (diluted 1 to 6) is used occasionally, but the chemicals most frequently used include:

Hydrochloric acid (diluted 2 to 3, or 2 to 5)
Nitric acid (diluted 1 to 2)
Ammonium hydroxide (ammonia, diluted 1 to 2)
Borax
Sodium carbonate (washing soda)
Cobalt nitrate
Salt of phosphorous
Potassium iodide
Sulfur

The acids and ammonium hydroxide should be purchased or ordered at a local drugstore, since these liquids cannot be sent through the mails. Acids are sold in concentrated form and must be diluted for use. When diluting acid, it is important to remember that *acid should always be added to the water,* NEVER the other way around. All acids should be treated with respect. They are best stored under lock and key if there are small children in the house. Although borax and sodium carbonate are available at almost any supermarket, other dry reagents must usually be ordered from a chemical supplier.

Descriptions of the chemical tests used in identifying a particular mineral can be found in most books of descriptive mineralogy.

TESTING MINERALS WITH HYDROCHLORIC ACID

Hydrochloric acid is particularly useful in identifying various carbonate minerals. For example, a drop of the dilute acid placed on calcite will effervesce readily, giving off carbon dioxide. Dolomite, however, which closely resembles calcite, does not react readily to cold acid and will effervesce only when crushed to a fine powder.

Small fragments of the mineral being tested should be placed in a test tube with enough hydrochloric acid to cover them. Note the reaction. Some carbonates dissolve rapidly in cold acid, others more slowly; still others dissolve only when the acid is heated. Some sulfides and oxides will decompose slowly in hydrochloric acid, giving off characteristic odors. Natrolite also dissolves, leaving a jellylike residue that serves to identify it. Copper minerals will stain acid solutions blue or green, while cobalt minerals turn solutions pink.

BLOWPIPE TESTS

A blowpipe is essentially a tapered brass tube fitted at one end with a funnel-shaped mouthpiece. It is used in conjunction with a gas burner or alcohol lamp to make various chemical tests on minerals. Blowing through the tube produces a thin stream of air which, when directed into a flame, increases the rate of combustion. Blowpiping requires a certain amount of practice before a steady flow of air into the flame can be maintained for longer than a few seconds.

The intensely hot, needle-pointed flame produced by the blowpipe is useful in determining how readily a mineral will melt. The *degree of fusibility* of a mineral is an important means of identification. Some minerals fuse easily in the blowpipe flame; others, such as quartz, are infusible. Seven minerals of varying fusibility have been selected as a scale against which the fusibility of all other minerals can be compared. When a particular mineral is said to fuse at 2, this means that its degree of fusibility is about the same as chalcopyrite, the mineral that is No. 2 in the fusibility scale.

Scale of Fusibility

1. Stibnite—Easily fused in a candle flame.
2. Chalcopyrite—Easily fused in a blowpipe flame.
3. Almandite Garnet—Less easily fused in a blowpipe flame.
4. Actinolite—Edges fuse with little difficulty in blowpipe flame.
5. Orthoclase—Edges fuse with difficulty in blowpipe flame.
6. Bronzite—Only the very thinnest edges will fuse.
7. Quartz—Infusible in a blowpipe flame.

Only a very thin, sharply pointed fragment of a mineral is used in testing fusibility. The mineral fragment, known as the *assay,* is grasped with forceps and held in the reducing part of the blowpipe flame (Figure 31) just above the inner cone. The reducing flame takes oxygen from the specimen. If a mineral is fusible, it melts and rounds over. On fusing, some minerals become magnetic or display phosphorescence; vermiculite *exfoliates,* opening out like the pages of a book.

Once the composition of a mineral is known, there is little difficulty in identifying it. The elements present in a mineral can sometimes be determined by fusing a sample onto a piece of charcoal. Standard blocks of charcoal about 4 inches long by 2 inches wide and ½ inch thick are used for this purpose.

Jadite, prized as a gemstone, has been used for carving since prehistoric times. This jadite owl comes from China. *Hoppock Associates*

The mineral sample to be tested must first be ground to a fine powder with a mortar and pestle. The powder is then placed in a pea-sized depression scooped out of the charcoal. It may be necessary to moisten the powdered sample with a bit of saliva to prevent it from being scattered by the blowpipe flame. If a metal is present in the mineral, a small bead or globule of the metal will be recovered by fusing or melting the sample with a *reducing flame* (Figure 31). The color and tenacity of the globule will serve to identify the element. Globules fused from iron, nickel, and cobalt compounds are also frequently magnetic. A metal globule may be obtained directly, or it may be necessary to use a flux in order to extract it from the mineral sample. Sodium carbonate mixed with charcoal makes an excellent flux for use in reductions.

When an oxidizing flame (Figure 32) is used for smelting the powdered sample, a characteristic coating, or *sublimate,* of oxide is often

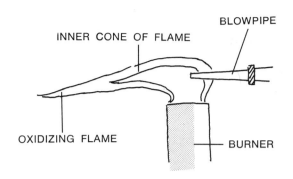

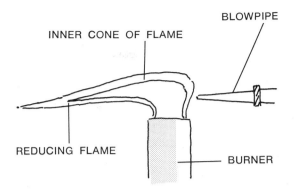

FIGURE 31 For a reducing flame, the blowpipe should be held directly behind the burner flame and the sample heated at the tip of the inner cone.

FIGURE 32 For an oxidizing flame, the blowpipe is held in the flame and the sample heated at the flame's tip.

produced on the charcoal. Many minerals are volatile when oxidized in a blowpipe flame; some also give off strong odors that help in identifying them. When potassium iodide and sulfur are used as a flux, even more characteristic sublimates can sometimes be obtained. As an aid to identification, most books of descriptive mineralogy include tables that list the colors of the various sublimates and metallic globules obtained in blowpipe tests. A block of plaster may be substituted for the charcoal if a sublimate is indistinct or difficult to identify against a black background.

TUBE TESTS

Glass tubing cut in about 6 inch lengths is used in making *open-tube tests*. A bit of the powdered mineral sample is inserted in a tube to a point about 2 inches from one end. The tube is then grasped in a wire test-tube holder and held in the flame of a Bunsen burner or alcohol lamp (Figure 33). It should be inclined at as sharp an angle as possible,

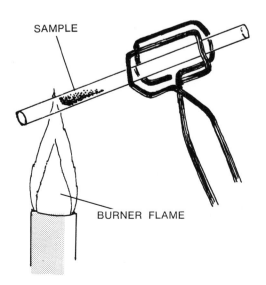

FIGURE 33 Open-tube method.

with the powdered sample at the lower end, just below the burner flame. As the sample is heated, the current of air flowing through the tube causes oxidation to take place and characteristic sublimates to collect on the inner walls of the tube. Gases may also be formed and these can be tested with moistened litmus paper held near the cooler end of the tube.

Although ¼-inch-diameter tubing is generally used for open-tube tests, glass tubing of a slightly smaller diameter (³⁄₁₆ inch or ⅛ inch) is better for *closed-tube tests*. The glass tubing is first cut into lengths of about 3 inches. One end of a tube should be fused closed, and the mineral sample to be tested placed at this end (Figure 34). The sample should be heated until red-hot and any reaction noted. Tables of open- and closed-tube test reactions are given in most mineralogy texts.

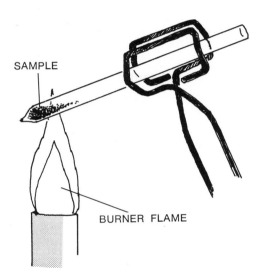

FIGURE 34 Closed-tube method.

BEAD TEST

A *bead test,* employing borax or salt of phosphorus as a flux, is also useful for identifying metallic elements. A short piece of platinum wire, with one end encased in a glass-rod holder and the other end bent to form a small loop, is needed for these tests. The loop of wire is heated in a burner flame until red-hot, then dipped into the powdered flux. A small amount of the flux will cling to the wire which is then returned to the flame and heated until a clear, glassy bead is formed in the loop. It may be necessary to dip the hot wire in the borax or salt of phosphorous several times in order to produce a bead that completely fills the loop. A few grains of the powdered mineral are then picked up by the hot bead which, when reheated in either an oxidizing or reducing flame, turns a characteristic color. On cooling, this color will change to another color which is also characteristic. The identity of the metal present in the mineral can be found by referring to a standard table of bead colors in a mineralogy text. The bead can be removed from the platinum wire by first heating it and then striking it sharply on a tabletop. Care should be taken to protect the work surface with an asbestos pad, since the hot beads will burn anything they touch.

FLAME TESTS

The same platinum wire used in the bead tests can also be used in making *flame tests,* but first it must be thoroughly cleaned of all bead residues which might alter the test results. It is usually easier to have two wires, with one reserved exclusively for flame tests. For best results, flame tests should be made in subdued light so that the colors produced in the burner flame can be plainly seen. The wire loop is first dipped in acid, then touched lightly to the powdered sample in order to pick up a few grains. When the wire is introduced into the burner flame, certain elements, if present in the mineral, will impart characteristic colors to the flame. It may be necessary to view the flame through a flame analyzer or cobalt-blue glass filter. These serve to absorb the yellow flame color of sodium that frequently masks the true colors of other elements.

Labeling and Cataloging Specimens

For a collection of minerals to have any scientific or monetary value, the specimens must be properly labeled and cataloged. Cataloging should be done as specimens are acquired and not left for some later time, since there is always the chance of field notes being lost and collecting localities forgotten. Most collectors use a cataloging system whereby each specimen is assigned a number which is recorded in a a catalog along with the essential information about the specimen. Some collectors prefer using a notebook or ledger as a catalog; others prefer a card file.

As a means of identification, the catalog number should be affixed to the specimen itself in some reasonably permanent manner. One method is to apply a tiny patch of quick-drying enamel to the underside of the specimen where it will not show. After the enamel has dried, the number is hand-lettered on the patch with India ink. A dab of clear varnish or lacquer is then applied to the patch to prevent the number from rubbing off. A very small gummed label might also be used, providing it too is given a protective coat of varnish or lacquer.

Besides the number, name of the mineral, and the date acquired, the entry in the catalog should also include the collecting locality, matrix and associations, cost (if specimen was purchased), and approximate value. The last is important in the event that the collection must be disposed of at some future time. Other important or interesting information about the specimen should be entered under "Remarks."

A label in the form of a small card should also be made up for each specimen. This label is usually placed alongside the specimen when it is displayed, or placed in the tray with the specimen if it is to be stored in a cabinet or box. Specimen labels can be typed, hand-lettered or commercially printed on standard card stock, the usual size being 1¼ by 2 inches. The catalog number, name of the species, chemical formula, and collecting locality should be shown on the label, as well as the name and address of the collector. When a specimen is to be placed in a competitive exhibition, the collector's name is, of course, omitted.

Storing Specimens

Once mineral specimens have been identified, cleaned, trimmed, and cataloged, they are ready to be placed in the permanent collection. It is usually impractical in a small home or apartment to display all the specimens. Most collectors reserve a few choice ones for display and store the bulk of their collections in cabinets or boxes. The type of cabinet used for storage will depend not only on the size of the specimens themselves, but also on the size of the collector's pocketbook. Fine wood or formica-clad cabinets specially designed to house mineral specimens are expensive, but they are a worthwhile investment for the serious collector. Some collectors who are handy with tools build their own storage cabinets or adapt second-hand cabinets for this purpose. Small chests of drawers or steel filing cabinets might also be used. Sturdy wood or cardboard boxes fitted with compartmented plastic trays are useful for storing small specimens.

Cabinet drawers should be partitioned in some manner to prevent the minerals from rubbing against one another. Shallow cardboard or plastic trays, available in standard specimen sizes, are excellent for dividing drawer space into appropriate compartments. Many collectors now use blocks of styrofoam plastic for holding specimens snugly in cabinet drawers. Specimens can be pressed into the surface of the styrofoam and thus kept from shifting around when the drawers are opened or closed.

In the home, minerals are best displayed in glass-walled or glass-fronted cabinets where they can be readily seen yet, at the same time, protected from dust and excessive handling. Depending on the space available, display cabinets can be either free-standing or hung on the wall.

Selected Bibliography

Books

BERRY, L. G., and MASON, B. *Mineralogy: Concepts, Descriptions, Determinations.* San Francisco: W. H. Freeman & Co., 1959.

DANA, E. S., and FORD, W. E. *A Textbook of Mineralogy,* 4th ed. New York: John Wiley & Sons, 1932.

————, and Hurlbut, C. S. *Manual of Mineralogy,* 17th ed. New York: John Wiley & Sons, 1959.

————. *Minerals and How to Study Them,* 3d ed. New York: John Wiley & Sons, 1949.

ENGLISH, G. L., and JENSEN, D. E. *Getting Acquainted with Minerals,* 2d ed. New York: McGraw-Hill Book Co., 1959.

FENTON, C. L. and M. A. *The Rock Book.* New York: Doubleday & Co., 1940.

GLEASON, S. *Ultraviolet Guide to Minerals.* Princeton, N. J.: D. Van Nostrand Co., 1960.

PIRSSON, L. V., and Knopf, A. *Rocks and Rock Minerals,* 3d ed. New York: John Wiley & Sons, 1947.

POUGH, F. H. *A Field Guide to Rocks and Minerals,* 3d ed. Boston: Houghton Mifflin Co., 1955.

SINKANKAS, J. *Gemstones and Minerals: How and Where to Find Them.* Princeton, N. J.: D. Van Nostrand Co., 1961.

————. *Mineralogy for Amateurs.* Princeton, N. J.: D. Van Nostrand Co., 1964.

SMITH, O. C. *Identification and Qualitative Chemical Analysis of Minerals,* 2d ed. Princeton, N. J.: D. Van Nostrand Co., 1953.

The following magazines regularly feature articles on minerals and mineral localities, and include advertisements and other information of interest to collectors:

Earth Science (bimonthly)
P. O. Box 1357
Chicago, Illinois

Gems and Minerals (monthly)
P. O. Box 687
Mentone, California

Lapidary Journal (bimonthly)
P. O. Box 2369
San Diego, California
(The expanded April issue of this magazine, known as the *Rockhound Buyers Guide*, will be of greatest interest to collectors.)

Rocks and Minerals (bimonthly)
P. O. Box 29
Peekskill, New York

Index